PHILIP'S

GUIDE TO THE NORTHERN CONSTELLATIONS

ROBIN SCAGELL

Contents

2 Introduction
4 Get your bearings
6 Spring signpost – the Great Bear
8 The Plough and Sickle
10 Summer signpost – the Swan
12 Summer sights
14 The Teapot and the Scorpion
16 Autumn signpost – Pegasus
18 Watery constellations
20 Winter signpost – Orion
22 The Bull and Seven Sisters
24 Winter wonders
26 The Solar System – Our star
27 The Moon
28 The Planets
31 Comets and comet-dust
32 Into the Universe
Acknowledgements

First published in Great Britain in 2004 by Philip's,
a division of Octopus Publishing Group Limited (ww
Carmelite House, 50 Victoria Embankment, London
An Hachette UK Company (www.hachette.co.uk)

Second edition 2018

Printed in United Kingdom

Details of other Philip's titles and services can be found on our website at: **www.philips-maps.co.uk**

Introduction

The night sky is a forgotten beauty for many people these days. Only when they escape from the cities or suburbs and suddenly discover that the canopy above them is brilliant with stars do they realize how much they have been missing. At such times they can feel lost – the familiar bland urban glow is replaced by a new and wonderful celestial landscape, with so many stars that there seems no hope of recognizing any pattern.

It is for those people that this book is intended. Learning the sky is really no different from finding your way about a new city. All you need are a few signposts, and after a while everything falls into place.

The book is divided into four sections, one for each season. In each case the major patterns act as signposts to the others. Follow the signposts over the year and you will find old favourites returning. Soon, the sky will be a lifelong friend.

Thousands of years ago our ancestors knew the skies well. They made up tales about the patterns of the stars, so that the heavens became a vast picturebook populated by fantastic creatures. Many of the star patterns, or constellations, that we use today originated in the Near East, some maybe before the start of recorded history. The stars of the Zodiac, through which the Sun, Moon and planets march, were already well established in Greek and Roman times. This book features just the major constellations – you can worry about the others once you know your way. On the maps, many of the less important stars are shown as grey to avoid confusion in identifying the constellations.

Towards the end of the book you will learn that the stars themselves are distant suns, rather like our Sun, shining by their own light. The planets, however, are members of the Sun's family like the Earth and are much closer, endlessly orbiting the Sun. They have no light of their own, but simply reflect the Sun's light. So if you come across a bright star which is not on the maps, but is in one of the zodiacal constellations, it is probably a planet. With a bit of practice you will even be able to pick out which planet it is, just by its appearance. The Sun's path during the year, the ecliptic, defines the Zodiac more precisely, and is marked on the maps.

One other circle is important – the Milky Way. This fuzzy, pale band of light encircles the heavens, and is actually our own star system, the Galaxy, seen from inside. It is a pancake of stars, with our Sun and Solar System about halfway out from the middle.

Once you have come to know the stars, bear in mind that they are an endangered species – or at least, our view of them from the surface of the Earth is at risk. Light pollution can wipe them out from even rural areas, if careless lighting is allowed to spread. Sadly, the Milky Way is invisible from much of Europe. So make sure that your own lighting does not contribute to the problem, and spread the word. Let us hope that the glories of the skies will not just be something you read about in books.

The Plough is one of the best-known star patterns in the sky.

Get your bearings

This map shows the brighter stars that can be seen from most of Europe and North America. Not all the stars are visible at one time, however. To find roughly which area of the sky you can see on a particular evening, turn the map so that the month when you are looking is at the bottom.

Now the stars in the bottom part of the map are due south at 9 pm (or 10 pm when Summer Time is in force). The overhead point is roughly a third of the way up from the bottom. Stars at the top are below the northern horizon at this time. If you are unsure where south is, remember that the Sun is more or less due south at midday (1 pm in summer).

As the night progresses, you will notice that the stars in the south are moving slowly to the west (the right). The whole sky moves anticlockwise around the centre of the map, turning once in just under 24 hours. If you were to take a snapshot of the sky looking south at the same time each night, you would see that as the months go by, the constellations slip from left to right, until each has been on display, and after a year the sky has turned full circle.

The heavens are not really turning around the Earth. These slow movements are the result of the daily turning of the Earth on its axis, and its yearly orbit around the Sun.

Some stars, around the centre of the map, are visible all year round in various orientations, and are called circumpolar stars. The rest, however, sink below the horizon at times. The exact limit of the circumpolar stars depends on where you live. From the latitude of the Canary Islands, for example, the group known as the Plough is just below the northern horizon on summer evenings, while from London and farther north it is still visible, skirting the northern horizon.

A Philip's Planisphere is an excellent way of finding exactly which stars are visible at any time. It has a movable overlay showing the horizon at the chosen time.

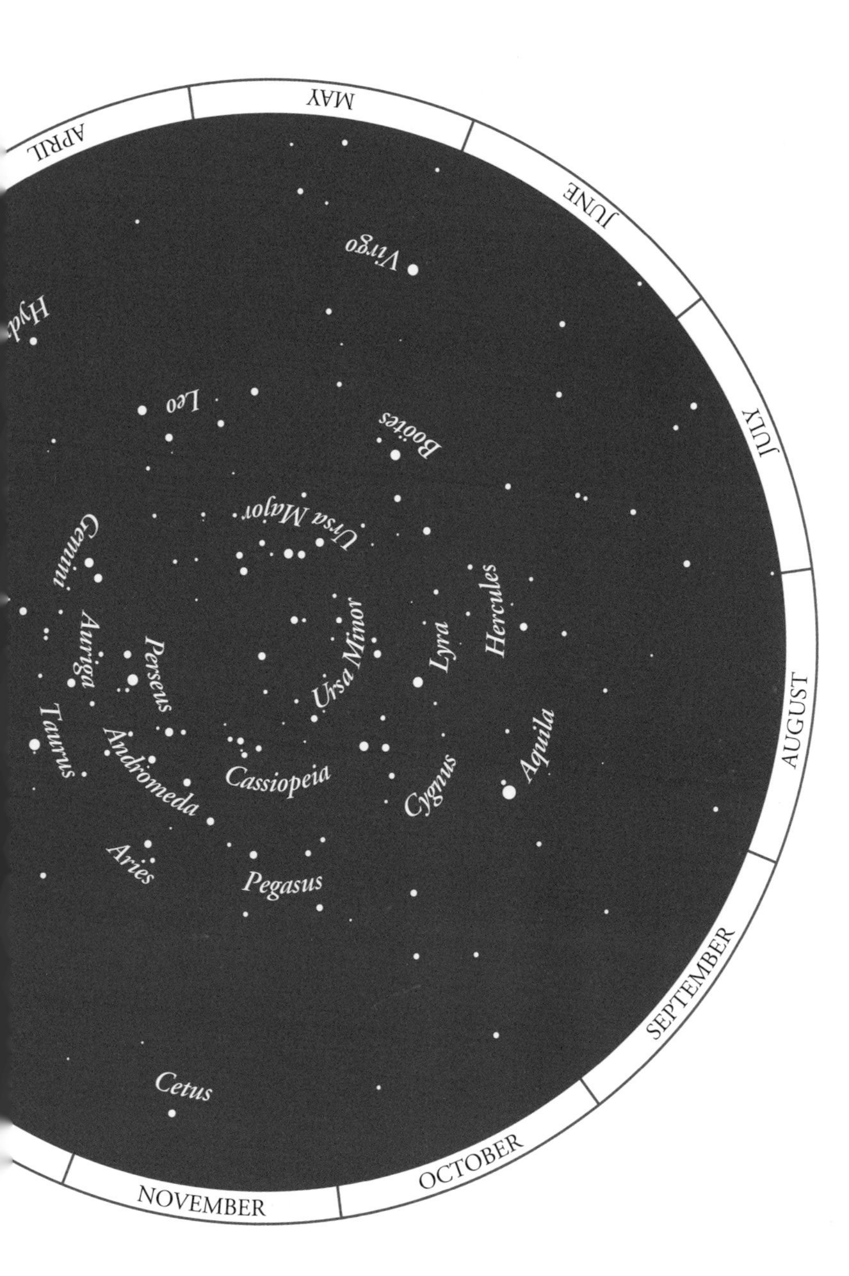
APRIL
MAY
JUNE
JULY
AUGUST
SEPTEMBER
OCTOBER
NOVEMBER
Virgo
Leo
Boötes
Ursa Major
Gemini
Auriga
Perseus
Ursa Minor
Lyra
Hercules
Taurus
Andromeda
Cassiopeia
Cygnus
Aquila
Aries
Pegasus
Cetus

Spring signpost – the Great Bear

If there is one star pattern that everyone knows, it is the Plough, known in North America as the Big Dipper. Though it is most obvious in autumn when it is low in the sky, in spring it is virtually overhead and makes a very useful signpost.

These days, its British name of the Plough means less to people than it once did, when the only old-fashioned ploughs are to be seen hanging on the walls of pubs of the same name. Similarly, its American name of the Big Dipper comes from its resemblance to the utensil that folk would use in the days before piped water. But call it the Saucepan and everyone will know what you mean. These seven stars are actually just the brightest in a larger group called Ursa Major, Latin for Great Bear.

The two stars at the right-hand edge of the Saucepan are known as the Pointers, because they point in the general direction of the Pole Star or Polaris. This is a moderately bright star that just happens to be close to the sky's north pole, around which the sky appears to turn. For this reason it is always in very nearly the same position in the sky from any given location. If you always observe from the same site, you will soon know exactly where to find the Pole Star because it hardly moves.

Many people expect the Pole Star to be brighter than it is, but what it lacks in brilliance it makes up for in usefulness. Find the Pole Star, using the Pointers as a guide, and you instantly know where north is. What is more, its angle above the horizon is the same as your latitude. In Oslo or Shetland, for example, which are at latitude 60°N, the Pole Star is 60° above the horizon. In London or Cologne it is about 51° up, while in Madrid, at latitude 40°N, it is 40° above the horizon. To early navigators, therefore, it was the most useful star in the sky. Pity the inhabitants of the southern hemisphere, who have no bright star marking the sky's south pole!

The Pole Star is at one end of a group of fainter stars called Ursa Minor, the Little Bear, and marks the end of its tail. Bears do not have long tails, but the celestial bears are the exception.

Follow the line from the Pointers down towards the horizon and you will come to another easily recognized constellation, Cassiopeia. Its five brightest stars form a 'W' shape. When the Plough is high, Cassiopeia is low in the sky, and vice versa. Together they swing round the sky with the Pole Star as their pivot, marking the changes in the seasons.

The approximate overhead point is marked on many maps with a cross, though its exact position will depend on your latitude.

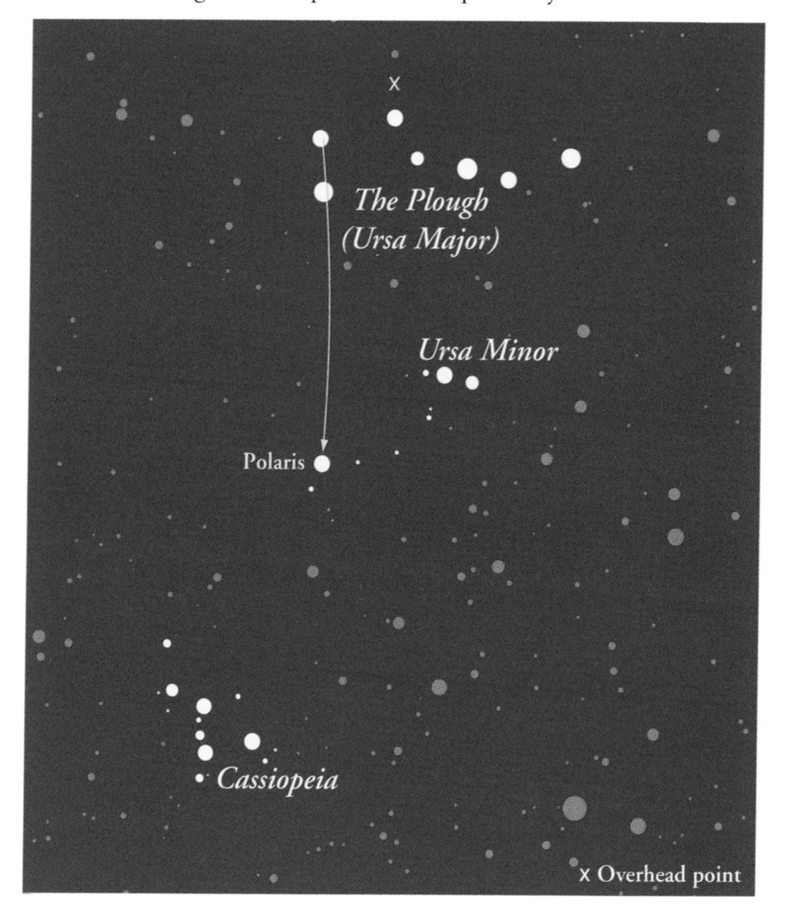

The Plough and Sickle

The Plough in spring makes an excellent signpost to other constellations. Follow its handle round in a curve and you come to one of the brightest stars in the sky, Arcturus, which is at the bottom of a fairly faint kite-shaped constellation called Boötes (pronounced 'bo-oh-teez'), the Herdsman. Keep going and you come to another bright star, Spica, in the constellation of Virgo, the Virgin. This is a roughly Y-shaped group of fairly faint stars with no obvious resemblance to a woman. Most people expect the constellations to work like 'join the dots' puzzles and remind you of their namesakes, but their names are more symbolic than representational.

Virgo happens to lie on the Zodiac. To ancient astrologers this gave it special significance, and the names of the constellations that lie along the Zodiac are known to everyone, even if the star groups themselves are sometimes insignificant. A good example of the latter is Libra, whose unremarkable stars lie to the lower left of Spica.

Below Virgo lies a small quadrilateral of stars, the brightest stars of Corvus, the Crow. In more overcrowded parts of the sky they would be lost, but here they stand out clearly, not far above the horizon. There is a reason why there are so few bright stars here. You are now looking out roughly at right angles to the Milky Way, where stars are sparse.

Go back to the Plough and use the Pointers to point southwards. This brings you to the stars of Leo, the Lion, one of the few constellations that actually looks like what it is supposed to be. A curve of stars marks the mane of the crouching lion, with a prominent pattern for its body. The curve is also known as the Sickle, which it strongly resembles. The brightest star in Leo, in the handle of the Sickle, is Regulus.

If your skies are fairly dark, look midway between the Sickle and Arcturus and you will come across a group of fairly faint stars that form a distinct cluster. This is Coma Berenices – the Hair of Berenice, who was an Egyptian queen. It is a genuine star cluster, and all its members would have formed together from a gas cloud that has long since disappeared. There are many similar clusters in the sky, but most need binoculars or a telescope to reveal them.

Summer signpost – the Swan

Your summer signpost is high in the sky, and is probably easiest to see when lying on your back. It is Cygnus, the Swan, also known as the Northern Cross. To find it, face south and first look for a white star virtually overhead, brighter than all the others in the area. This is Vega, in the rather small constellation of Lyra, the Lyre – the sky's only musical instrument. Cygnus lies to its left, with its brightest star, Deneb, at the top of a fairly large starry cross.

To the ancient Greeks, who named many of our constellations, this was Cygnus, the Swan. Deneb marks its tail, and its long neck stretches southwards towards the horizon. Its outstretched wings are the arm of the cross. This Northern Cross is much larger than the more famous Southern Cross, which is not visible from Europe.

The swan is flying along the line of the Milky Way. If you have a good, dark country sky you will be amazed at how brilliant the Milky Way can be. From many suburban areas, however, you can only glimpse the part that runs through Cygnus, where it is virtually overhead, in the darkest part of the sky. The brightest part of the Milky Way is lower down in Sagittarius, where it is often lost in the light pollution.

Even from the suburbs, though, you can glimpse the Milky Way by scanning this area with binoculars. It is just filled with stars, and in a good sky the effect is stunning. Every observer, no matter how experienced, gets a thrill out of simply stargazing at the Milky Way through binoculars.

The Milky Way seems to divide in two in Cygnus. This Great Rift or Cygnus Rift is actually a dust cloud within our local spiral arm of the Galaxy, hiding the stars beyond.

The stars we see are all of different brightnesses, and Cygnus contains some good examples. Deneb is a truly brilliant star, some 60,000 times as bright as the Sun, but it is so far away that its light, travelling at 300,000 km/sec, takes over 3000 years to reach us. That is, it is 3000 light years away.

In contrast, 61 Cygni, another famous star in Cygnus, is one of the closest to us. It is shown on the map, and can be found with a bit of searching. 61 Cygni was the first star to have its distance measured, in 1838, and it is just over 11 light years away. What we see as one star to the naked eye is actually a pair of stars, each about a tenth of the Sun's brightness. Despite being so close to us, 61 Cygni is barely visible to the naked eye.

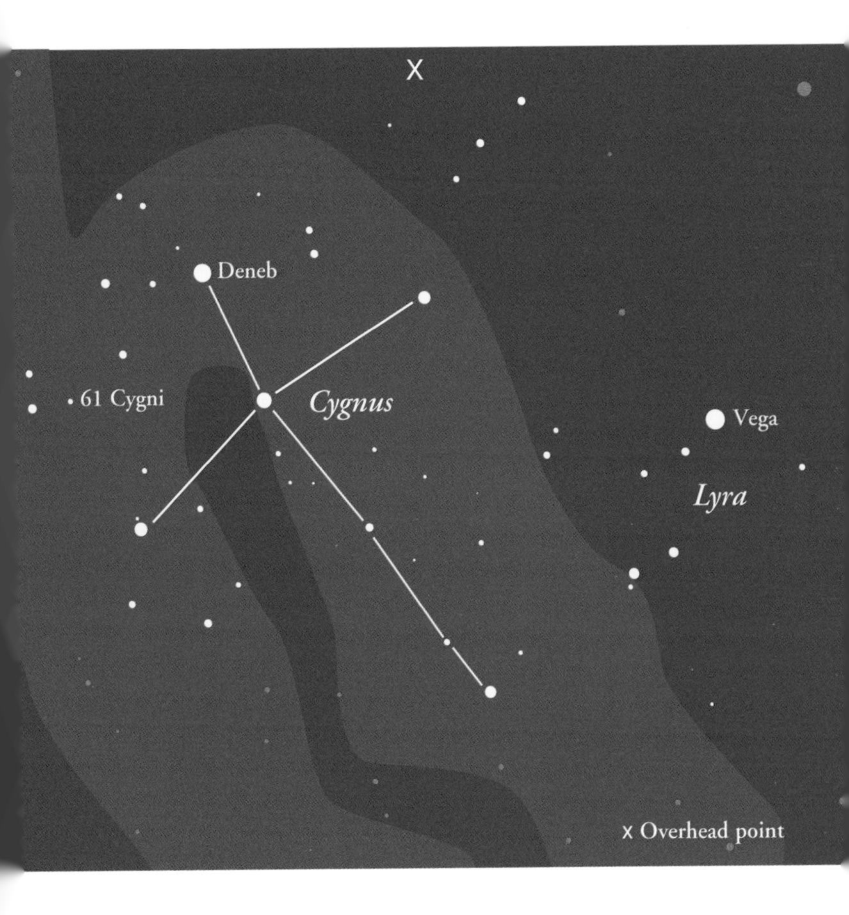

Summer sights

Deneb and Vega are two stars of what is generally called the Summer Triangle. The third, Altair, is roughly halfway between them and the horizon. You can easily identify it because it has two fainter stars flanking it, forming a straight line that points towards Vega. It is the brightest star in Aquila, the Eagle.

Using Cygnus and the Summer Triangle, you can locate many other constellations. Midway between Altair and the head of Cygnus, for example, is a lovely little constellation called Sagitta, the Arrow. Fortunately this arrow has missed the two birds, and it is sailing harmlessly between them.

Look with binoculars just to the right of the arrow and you can see a group of stars known as the Coathanger. This is not a constellation in its own right – it actually lies in Vulpecula, the Little Fox – but it is a very popular object because of its shape. It is picked out in a magnified view on the map.

A small constellation that again looks like what it is meant to be is to the left of Altair. This is Delphinus, the Dolphin, and it is not hard to make out its shape as it leaps out of the water, as if it were putting on a display at a theme park.

Return to Vega, and investigate its constellation of Lyra, which is a small parallelogram of stars. Vega forms a small triangle with two fairly faint stars, just a couple of fingers' breadths away. The upper of these is a famous star – the Double Double. If you have good eyesight, you should be able to see that it is in fact two stars. In a telescope, with quite a high magnification, each of these stars is seen to be a double star in its own right. The Double Double is one of the most celebrated double stars in the sky. The two pairs of stars are in orbit around each other, taking hundreds of years to complete a single orbit.

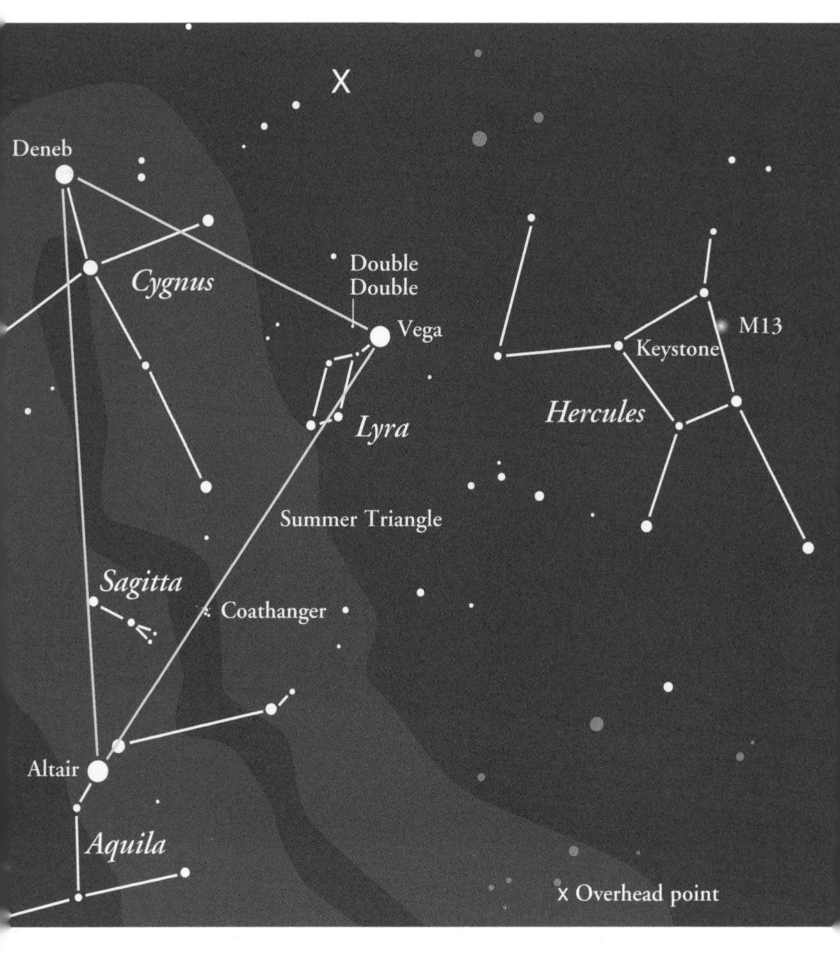

Take a line from Deneb through Vega and you find a quite undistinguished constellation, Hercules, with its wedge of stars, known as the Keystone. This is home to one of the showpieces of the northern sky, the globular cluster M13, a ball of about a million stars. It has to be said that in binoculars M13 is a small and disappointing sight, but in a modest-sized telescope it is a favourite object for amateur astronomers.

The Teapot and the Scorpion

Even if the Milky Way is not visible, you can follow its path towards the horizon by using Cygnus to point the way. Fairly close to the horizon lies Sagittarius, the Archer. While it does not look remotely like the centaur with a bow and arrow that mythology dictates, it is a dead ringer for a much more familiar object – a teapot. It is pointing downwards, as if its spout is pouring tea down the Milky Way, and to add to the illusion, the Milky Way is particularly bright here, looking like a cloud of steam from the spout.

Oddly, although the centre of the Galaxy lies in Sagittarius, just south of the steam from the teapot, the Milky Way in that direction is dim. This is because of the dense clouds of gas and dust that lie along the plane of the Milky Way, like the meat in a hamburger. They hide the centre from our gaze.

If you could travel way outside the Milky Way Galaxy, you would see that it has a central bulge, from which spreads a flat disc with a spiral shape. The Sun lies in one of the arms of the spiral.

The spiral arms are home to huge numbers of stars, clusters and nebulae. The word nebula (plural nebulae, which astronomers pronounce 'nebu-lee') is Latin for cloud. One good example is the Lagoon Nebula, which is visible with the naked eye or binoculars as a small misty patch some way to the north of the teapot's spout.

To the right of Sagittarius is a bright star that even a casual glance shows is pale orange. This is Antares, at the heart of Scorpius, the Scorpion. A beautiful curving line of stars to its southeast marks its tail, though much of this is below the horizon from all but the extreme south of Europe. Scorpius is a true celestial scorpion, complete with sting.

Antares is what is called a red supergiant star. Most stars turn into red giants at a late stage in their life, and Antares is a particularly massive example. Put in the Sun's place, it would spread out to the orbit of Jupiter.

Some time in the future, probably millions of years from now, it will change again, this time flaring up as a supernova, a truly awesome stellar explosion. When Antares turns supernova, it will outshine every star in the sky apart from the Sun.

No supernova has been seen in our Galaxy since 1604. The next one to appear will probably not be Antares, but some currently undistinguished star. When it happens, the startled world will wonder at the awful and unexpected glare from the heavens.

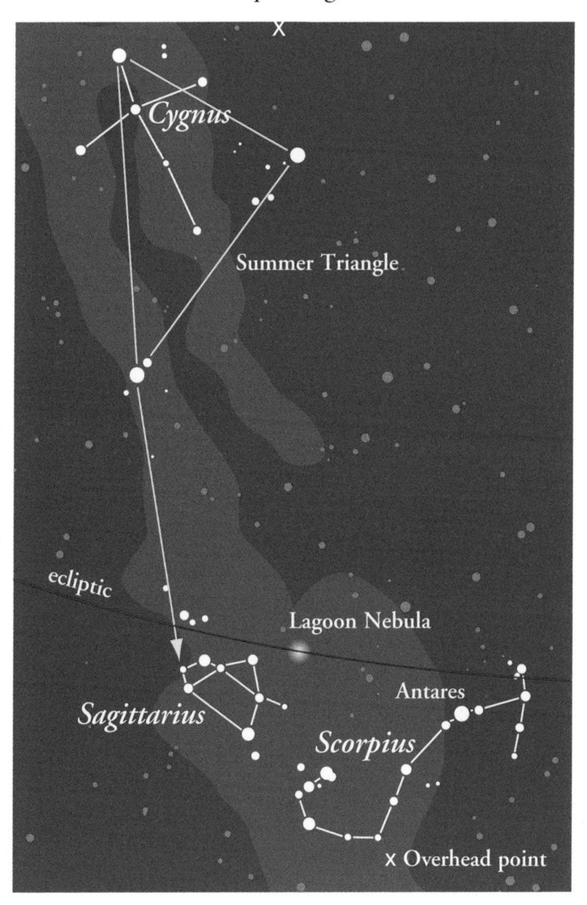

Autumn signpost – Pegasus

Autumn sees the Milky Way slipping down towards the west, though the Summer Triangle remains on view well into the dark nights of the winter. Again there is an absence of bright stars in the sky. This season's signpost is in the southern part of the sky – the Square of Pegasus.

Although this is a well-known sky pattern, its stars are not particularly bright, nor are they a perfect square. But because there are so few stars in this part of the sky, it is not too hard to find. Look about halfway up the sky to the south and you will see the Square, which is actually quite large – about as wide as your outstretched hand at arm's length.

Pegasus is a mythological winged horse, but in one of those unexplained mysteries of the sky, not only is it just the front end of the horse, but it is also usually depicted upside down.

To add to the indignity, Pegasus shares the upper left-hand star of the Square with its neighbouring constellation, Andromeda. This star is the westernmost of a line of stars in Andromeda, and it marks the starting point of a short trail to one of the most famous objects in the sky – the Andromeda Galaxy, also known as M31.

Use the map to pick out this line of stars, which are like an upwards curving extension of the top of the Square. Count two stars along, then two faint stars at right angles to the north. Just beyond the second of these two stars is the Andromeda Galaxy. In a clear sky it is easy to see with the naked eye, but it is visible even from city centres with binoculars if you get away from immediate lights, such as in a park.

The Andromeda Galaxy looks like an oval blur of light. In a dark sky it is quite large and prominent, but even in a poor sky you can see the central parts.

It is another spiral galaxy, almost a twin of our own. It lies a staggering 2.5 million light years away, which means that the light you are seeing now left it at a time when the hominid ancestors of the human race walked on the Earth.

The Andromeda Galaxy is the most distant object visible with the naked eye. From it, our own Galaxy would appear more or less as it does to us. What alien eyes are looking at us right now – and seeing the Milky Way as it was in the distant past?

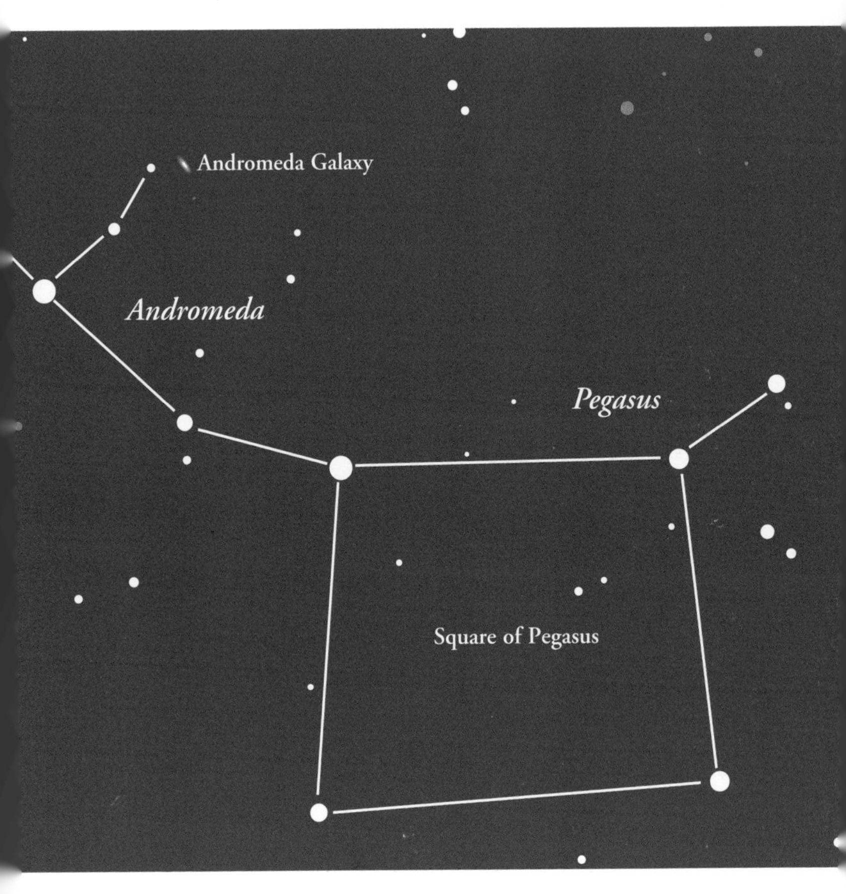

Watery constellations

Anyone with a special affinity for the zodiacal constellations Aquarius or Pisces must feel a bit disappointed that 'their' constellations are not more obvious. Though they are quite large, neither of them have any bright stars. Take the diagonal of the Square of Pegasus down to the southwest and you arrive at the top of Aquarius, the Water Carrier. Its most distinctive feature is a little pattern of five stars known as the Water Jar, though to our eyes it might look more like a jet plane. The rest of Aquarius's stars sprawl down to the southwest, where it meets the even less distinguished constellation of Capricornus.

Pisces consists of two long ragged lines of even fainter stars to the southeast of the Square, representing two fish. But the most distinctive part of Pisces is directly under the Square – a little pattern known as the Circlet, which represents the head of one of the fish. In many suburban skies, Pisces may be all but invisible.

Two other watery constellations in this part of the sky are easier to see. Follow the right-hand edge of the Square down to the southern horizon and you encounter a bright star, Fomalhaut. This is the main star of the otherwise indistinguished constellation of Piscis Austrinus, the Southern Fish. From northern Europe, this star may be impossible to see – from Oslo, for example, it rises barely a degree above the southern horizon, though from southern Britain it is easily visible.

Taking the left-hand edge of the Square brings you to a moderately bright star, Deneb Kaitos, the main star in Cetus, the Whale. The other stars of Cetus extend away to its upper left. One of them, Mira, varies widely in brightness and more often than not is below naked-eye visibility.

Projecting the left side of the Square of Pegasus upwards takes you to the 'W' of Cassiopeia, which is virtually overhead at this time of year. The Milky Way arches right across the sky, and is full of stars and star clusters. Use the bright line of Andromeda's stars to lead you to Perseus, another mythological character. This constellation is shaped like an italic 'T'.

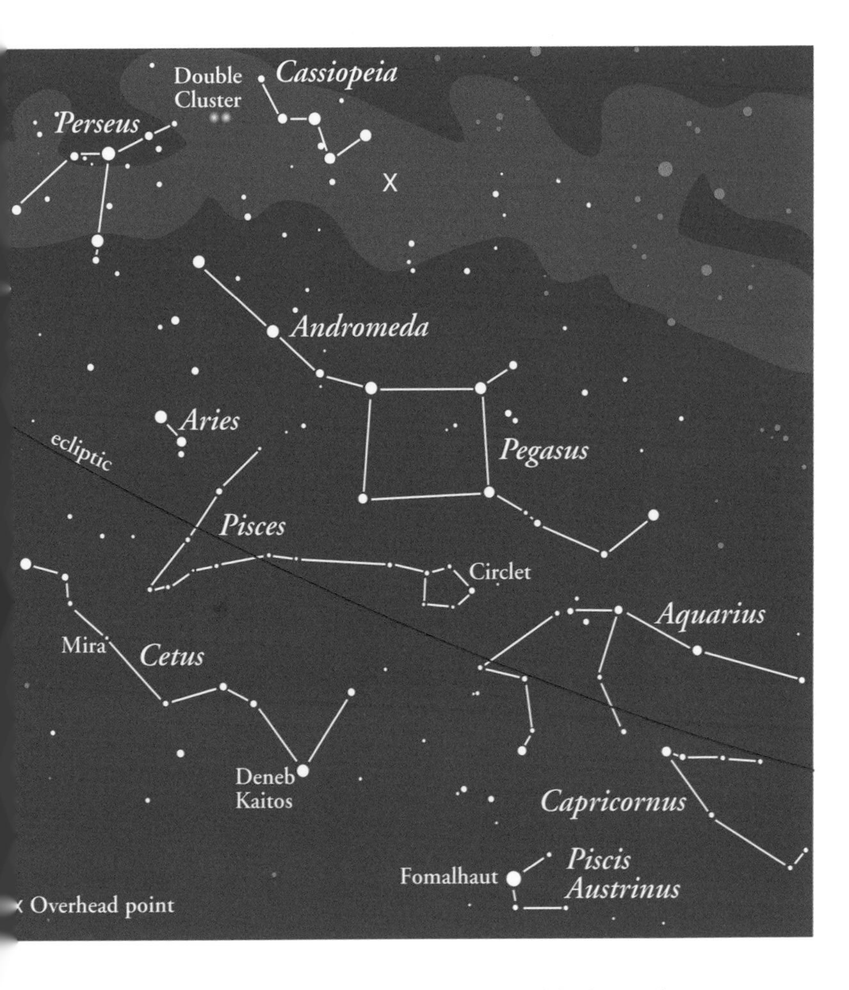

Between Perseus and Cassiopeia lies one of the best sights in the sky for binoculars and small telescopes, the Double Cluster. You can see a fuzzy patch with the naked eye even from suburban skies, but with any optical aid it is transformed into a pair of glittering star clusters. Either cluster would be a jewel in its own right, but together they are a glorious spectacle.

Winter signpost – Orion

This season's signpost is one of the most splendid constellations of all – Orion, the Hunter. He marches high in the south, with his glittering belt of three stars in a line making him unmistakable. Flanking these are the red giant star Betelgeuse to the upper left and the blue-white star Rigel to the lower right.

Betelgeuse is one shoulder of the hunter, while Rigel is a foot as he advances towards the celestial Bull, which is shown on page 23. A curving line of faint stars marks his shield. But his most magical armament is his sword, hanging from his belt.

The middle of the line of stars forming his sword is clearly misty, even to the naked eye. This is the Orion Nebula, known to astronomers as a birthplace of stars. Turn a pair of binoculars on the nebula and you can see some of the recently born stars glowing among the wreaths of gas from which they formed. By recent, astronomers mean over the past million or so years. Don't expect to see another one appear as you watch!

Orion's belt points downwards and to the left to Canis Major, the larger of his two dogs. Such a signpost is hardly necessary, for Canis Major contains the brightest star in the sky, Sirius – also called the Dog Star. Canis Major does actually resemble a sort of stick-dog, with Sirius marking its neck and the triangle of stars to the south being a hind leg and the tail.

Sirius is so bright in our sky mainly because it is one of the closest stars, only 8.3 light years away. True, it is brighter than the Sun by 25 times, but by star standards this is a trifling difference. Take Sirius to the distance of the Orion Nebula, say, and it would disappear from view below naked-eye visibility.

The white brilliance of Sirius masks from view its faint companion, Sirius B – dubbed 'the Pup'. If it were not close to Sirius, the Pup would be visible using a small telescope, but in practice astronomers need special techniques to study it. Sirius B is one of a very strange group of stars known as the white dwarfs.

From its motion around Sirius, the Pup is known to be about as massive as the Sun, yet it only has approximately 1/500 its brightness. This means that it must have a diameter not much more than twice that of the Earth, which makes it incredibly dense – about 125,000 times the density of water. Put another way, a nail made of the same material as Sirius B would weigh about as much as a man.

How did a star get into this condition? When a star like the Sun ages, after it turns into a red giant, its power output declines and it can no longer support its own weight. So it collapses down to the size of a planet and becomes a white dwarf, a faint relic of its former self. In billions of years, this will happen to the Sun.

The Bull and Seven Sisters

Follow Orion's belt northwards, to the upper right, and it points to an orange star – another red giant, Aldebaran. This marks the angry red eye of Taurus, the Bull, whose head is neatly outlined by a V-shape of stars called the Hyades (pronounced 'high-a-deez'). These stars are a genuine cluster, but the best-known cluster of all is found by continuing the line past Aldebaran.

This cluster is the Pleiades (pronounced 'ply-a-deez'), also known as the Seven Sisters. Even though none of these stars are particularly bright, they catch the eye straight away, looking as if they are enveloped in mist. This is because there are many fainter stars that cannot be seen individually by eye, but which add to the light of the cluster.

Even with the naked eye, many people can see more than seven stars – but seven was a popular number in ancient times. Binoculars show many more. The Pleiades were born together some 70 million years ago.

To the upper left of Taurus in the northern sky is another ancient constellation, Auriga, the Herdsman. There is an obvious pentagon of stars, with the bright, orange Capella at its top, although the bottom star of the pentagon is officially shared with Taurus.

The Milky Way runs through Auriga, and along the middle of the constellation is a line of three star clusters, numbered M36, M37 and M38. In a good dark sky you might almost think you have spotted a faint new comet as your eye is drawn to them. Binoculars or a small telescope, however, show them as true star clusters, each containing hundreds of stars.

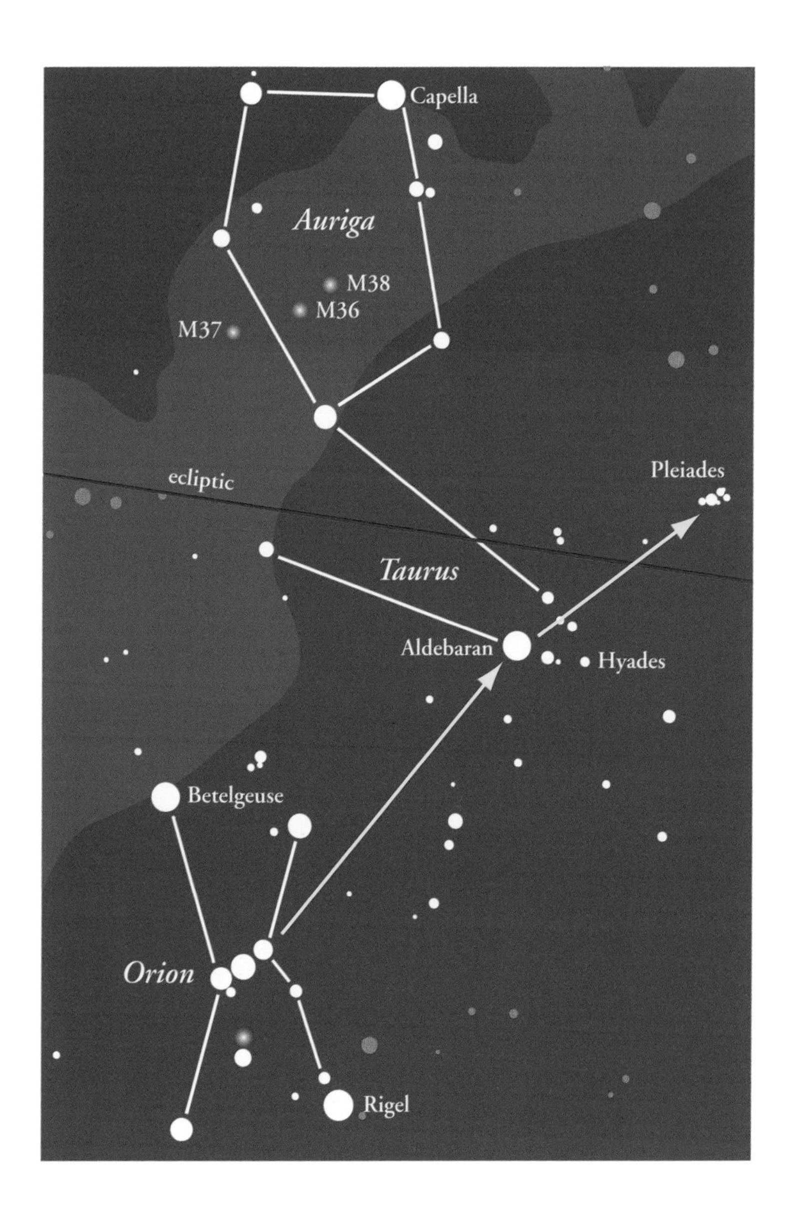
Capella
Auriga
M38
M36
M37
ecliptic
Pleiades
Taurus
Aldebaran
Hyades
Betelgeuse
Orion
Rigel

Winter wonders

Follow the line from Rigel through Betelgeuse and you arrive at an unmistakable pair of stars, which not surprisingly are Gemini, the Twins. Their names are Castor and Pollux, and one way to remember which is which is that Pollux is closest to Procyon, while Castor is closest to Capella. Pollux is the brighter of the two.

Castor is one of those stars beloved of amateur astronomers as a test of a small telescope because it is in fact a double star. In the 20th century it was regarded as quite a severe test to be able to separate the two stars with dark sky between them, but now it is easier to see with a small telescope. This is not because telescopes are getting better, but because the separation between the two stars is slowly widening as they orbit each other every 470 years.

There is a third, fainter star in the system, and in fact each of the three stars is itself a double star, though the components are too close to be seen. So Castor is not actually a single star, but six.

Take a line to the left across the shoulders of Orion and you come to the lesser of his two dogs, the constellation of Canis Minor. Its bright star, Procyon, like Sirius, has a white dwarf companion.

Making a triangle with Pollux and Procyon is Cancer, the Crab, the faintest of all the constellations of the Zodiac. It probably exists only because the ancient astrologers needed to divide the sky into 12, but it still manages to attract attention because it contains a fine star cluster. Though not as brilliant as the Pleiades, the cluster is nevertheless bright enough to be visible even in a fairly poor sky, and it is a delightful sight in

binoculars or telescope. Its catalogue number is M44, but it has two popular names – the Beehive cluster, and Praesepe, which means Manger.

Immediately below Cancer is a small star pattern that marks the head of the largest constellation in the sky. This group of six or so stars forms the head of Hydra, the Water Snake, which wriggles across the southern sky and finishes up below Spica in the constellation of Virgo. The brightest star in Hydra, Alphard, is to the lower left of the head. Its name is Arabic for 'the Solitary One', and it is well deserved because it shines almost alone in this barren part of the sky.

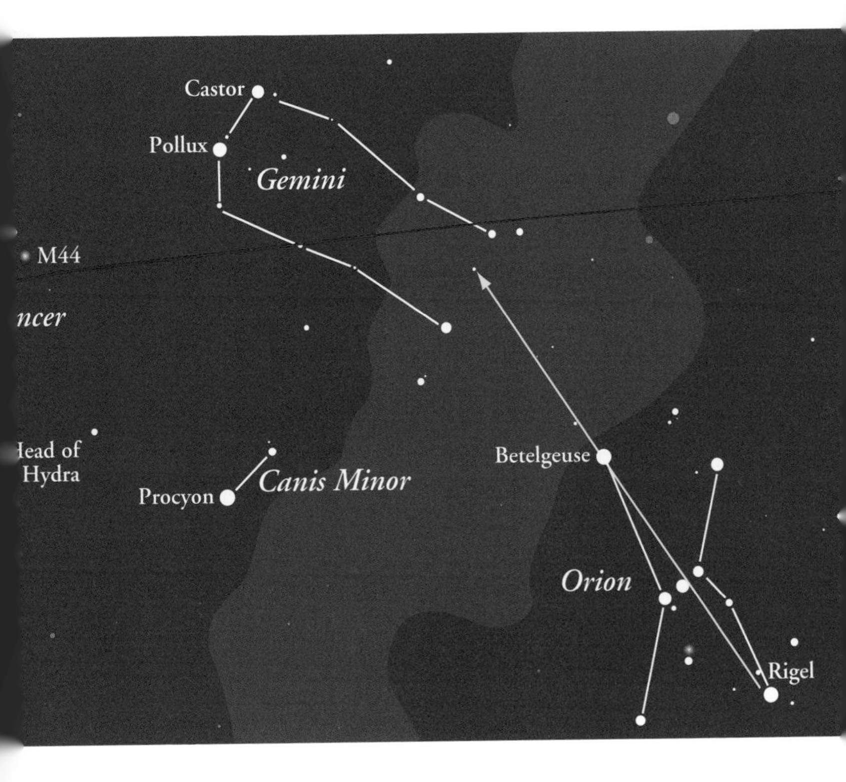

The Solar System

Our star

The Sun is so familiar to us that we rarely think of it as an astronomical body. But in reality it is a star – a Goldilocks sort of star, neither too big and hot, nor too small and cool. People often describe it as yellow, but it is actually pure white. When you sometimes glimpse it through cloud, or when it is low in the sky, its light is filtering through absorbing layers which make it look yellow.

Not that you should ever look directly at the Sun, of course. Its full light will do permanent eye damage, and astronomers take special precautions when studying it. Please do not take chances with improvised filters, either.

The Sun shares in the apparent movement of the sky, rising in the eastern sky, moving round to a high point in the south and setting in the western sky. Its brilliance hides the stars, but they are still there during the day.

Our own star is nearly 150 million km away from us and 1,400,000 km across. It is not solid, but is made up of gas – mostly hydrogen and some helium. Deep inside, nuclear reactions similar to those in a hydrogen bomb continually transform hydrogen into helium, releasing energy as they do so. This energy eventually reaches the surface, making it shine brilliantly.

This energy production means that the Sun is losing mass all the time (mass is the amount of material in a body – its weight depends on where you measure it). In fact, it is losing 4 million tonnes a second, which might sound worrying. But there is so much material in the Sun that it has been shining for about 5000 million (5 billion) years, and will continue to do so for another 5 billion.

Despite its temperature of 6000°C, the Sun's surface is not unblemished. In some places, magnetic fields restrict the light output, resulting in sunspots which appear darker than the rest of the Sun. At some times these are plentiful and at others they are scarce, the numbers varying on a roughly 11-year cycle.

The Moon

These days there are hundreds of artificial satellites orbiting the Earth, some of which can be seen as moving points of light crossing the sky in late twilight. But the Moon is our only natural satellite, and its orbit around the Earth takes 29 days to complete.

Many people are unfamiliar with the sequence of the Moon's phases, which are caused by the changing angle of the Sun's illumination as the Moon travels in its orbit. The New Moon is a thin crescent, visible soon after sunset, while a few days later it is a half moon, known as First Quarter because it is a quarter of the way around its orbit. A week later it is Full, and rises more or less opposite the setting Sun. Seven days or so after that it is at Last Quarter, in the early morning sky, and before the lunar month is up it is a thin crescent again, this time just before sunrise.

The Moon, at about 400,000 km away, is much closer than the Sun, so what happens when it passes in front of it? Usually it goes above or below the Sun as seen in the sky, but when it does go exactly in front, the Sun's light is blocked and we see an eclipse of the Sun. These are quite rare, as you have to be in exactly the right place to see them, but more common are eclipses of the Moon, when the Moon passes through the Earth's shadow.

Next time you see the Moon, study it carefully. With average eyes you can see a surprising amount of detail on its 3476 km globe. The dark patches are vast plains of solidified lava – once-molten rock that flooded out from the interior billions of years ago when huge chunks of space debris pounded its surface. They were called 'seas' by astronomers hundreds of years ago and the name has stuck.

Some of the brighter patches are craters, formed later in its history. Even a small pair of binoculars turns the Moon into a fantastic landscape of craters, plains and mountains. It is one of the great spectacles of the sky.

The Planets

MANY VOLCANOES ERUPT MULBERRY JAM SANDWICHES UNTIL NOVEMBER. No, that is not really true, but it is a good way to remember the names of the planets in order outwards from the Sun: Mercury, Venus, Earth, Mars, Jupiter, Saturn, Uranus and Neptune. The planets divide neatly into two groups – the first four are small, dense, rocky planets and the rest are much larger but made of lightweight materials.

Each planet has a distinctive appearance, and if you see a bright star near the ecliptic that is not on the maps, the chances are that it is a planet. Another important difference is that,

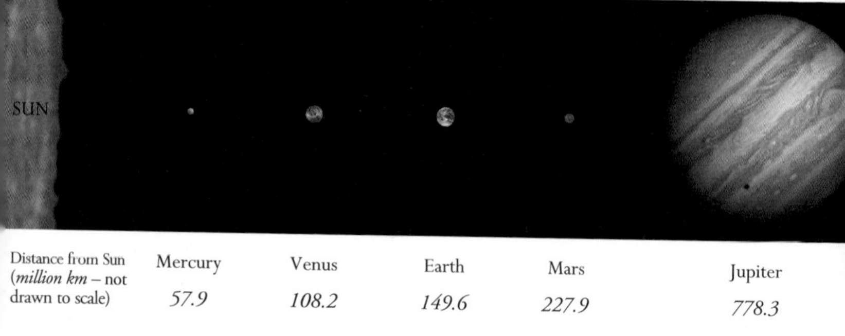

Distance from Sun (*million km* – not drawn to scale)	Mercury	Venus	Earth	Mars	Jupiter
	57.9	*108.2*	*149.6*	*227.9*	*778.3*

unlike stars, the planets rarely twinkle. Twinkling is caused by air currents in our atmosphere, and it affects points of light, such as stars, more than planets, which have a small diameter in the sky.

Mercury is a slippery customer. Because it is so close to the Sun it is only ever visible low in the twilight sky – and then only for a week or so at a time. It is whitish, and although quite bright is often hard to see in the twilight. Venus is another matter. Though it, too, is only to be seen on one side or other of the Sun, it is very much brighter – the brightest object in the sky after the Sun and Moon. Its almost dazzling white light is a truly beautiful sight against a deepening blue twilight sky. The planet's brightness is a result of being completely cloud-covered, so that it reflects light very well.

Mars is the next planet out from Earth, so it and the rest of the planets may be seen along any part of the ecliptic. Its pale orange colour is unmistakable, and is caused by the reddish rocks on its surface. At times, when it is closest to Earth, it is brighter than any star.

Did life once form on Mars? Today it is a freezing desert, but there are signs that billions of years ago it was warmer and even had surface water. Maybe there are traces of early life lurking under the red rocks.

Saturn *1427* Uranus *2871* Neptune *4497*

Jupiter, the largest planet, is second in brightness only to Venus and appears slightly more cream coloured. At 143,000 km it has over a tenth of the diameter of the Sun itself, and contains as much mass as 318 Earths. If Jupiter were made of rock, like Earth, it would be so massive that most of the other planets would be tugged into it by the pull of its gravity. Fortunately, it consists mostly of the lightest elements, hydrogen and helium, for Jupiter is a giant ball of gas. What looks like its surface is only the cloud tops. These have a banded appearance, with darker belts and ever-changing spots and streaks.

Turn binoculars on Jupiter and you will see the four largest of its moons, though not all of them may be visible at once. Look an hour or so later and you may see a change in their positions as they orbit the planet.

It so happens that Jupiter takes nearly 12 years for one orbit of the Sun, so each year it moves through roughly one zodiacal constellation eastward.

Saturn, another gas giant, is slightly yellowish, and is fainter than Jupiter, though it is still brighter than most stars. Rather smaller than Jupiter and with much paler markings, it would definitely be its poor relation if it were not for its amazing rings. These can be seen in even a small telescope, completely encircling the planet. They are not solid, but consist of millions of ice and rock particles, all orbiting in a flat plane.

Saturn is quite remote from the Sun, and plods around it in 30 years. So its eastward trek can be followed over years rather than months.

Even more distant are the remaining planets, Uranus and Neptune. To find these you will need binoculars and an accurate knowledge of their positions.

Comets and comet-dust

The appearance of a bright comet creates great excitement. They are quite rare, and can be dramatic, with a starlike head and a streamer of a tail, hanging motionless in the sky. They move from night to night against the starry background, and in a few days or sometimes weeks they are gone from view.

Comets are really quite tiny members of the Solar System, orbiting the Sun, usually in elongated paths. The main body of even a large comet is only a few tens of kilometres across, which would normally be far too faint to be seen. But because comets are made largely of ice, when they come close to the Sun some of their surface layer turns to gas, and dust mixed in with the gas is set free. It is mostly the dust that is visible as a tail, spreading out in a great curving orbit around the Sun.

Bright comets usually appear with very little warning, because their orbits take thousands of years to complete. They spend most of their time at the edges of the Solar System and it is not until they come close to the Sun that we get to know about them.

The dust from a comet spreads out in a broad band along its orbit. The Solar System is full of these tiny specks from comets that appeared long ago and have long since melted away to nothing. If one speck happens to collide with the Earth, it burns up briefly in the upper atmosphere, leaving a streak of light high above us. This is a meteor, also known as a shooting star.

Usually there are only a few meteors visible every hour, but if the Earth passes through a thick part of the trail left by a comet, meteor numbers will increase. On some nights, particularly in autumn, meteors can appear more frequently.

Into the Universe

Our Solar System is just a small part of the huge collection of over 100 billion stars that we call the Milky Way Galaxy. All the stars we see with the naked eye are comparatively near neighbours, and the great river of the Milky Way is really millions of other, more distant suns in the Galaxy. But the Milky Way Galaxy is in turn just a single galaxy among billions of others, stretching away as far as our telescopes can detect.

The Andromeda Galaxy is a local neighbour, similar to our own galaxy. It and the Magellanic Clouds, visible from the southern hemisphere, are the only galaxies readily visible to the naked eye, but if our eyes could somehow see the others, they would be more plentiful than the stars.

The Hubble Space Telescope has taken long-exposure photographs of small regions of the sky, which show nothing but remote galaxies. The light from these has taken just a bit less than an eternity to reach us – it left them when the Universe was much younger. Giant telescopes are, in effect, time machines.

Some of the most distant objects are quasars, now agreed to be vast outpourings of energy at the hearts of primeval galaxies. They draw their power from black holes – dense concentrations of matter that act like plugholes in space. Just before stars fall into them and disappear from view altogether, they are torn apart in a blaze of energy that can be seen across the Universe.

Acknowledgements

My thanks to Frances Adlington of Philip's for seeing this book through the press. Chris Marriott's excellent SkyMap program was used for producing the star maps. The photograph of the Plough was taken by me. That of the Moon is copyright NASA/JPL/USGS. The Solar System illustration is based on images from NASA, ESA, JPL and the Hubble Space Telescope. Finally, a short commercial for the Society for Popular Astronomy, which exists to help people starting out in astronomy. For details, go to www.popastro.com.